A Gift of Wings

A Gift of Wings

By C.W. Gusewelle and Charles Porter, M.D.

Editor: Doug Weaver
Design and line art: Dorothy Day
Cover: Vicky Frenkel

Published by Kansas City Star Books.

First edition.

ISBN: 978-1-933466-45-3

Printed in the United States of America by Walsworth Publishing Co., Marceline, Missouri
To order copies, call StarInfo at (816) 234-4636 and say "BOOKS."

Order on-line at www.TheKansasCityStore.com.

A Gift of Wings

Photographs by Charles Porter, M.D.

Text by C.W. Gusewelle

Kansas City Star Books

This book is dedicated to all who
appreciate the wonders of Nature.

To wish for wings, if one hasn't them already, is both pointless and painful. If we creep now, we will not learn to fly.

That is what the caterpillar must think, too, if it thinks at all. The difference between us is that the caterpillar is wrong.

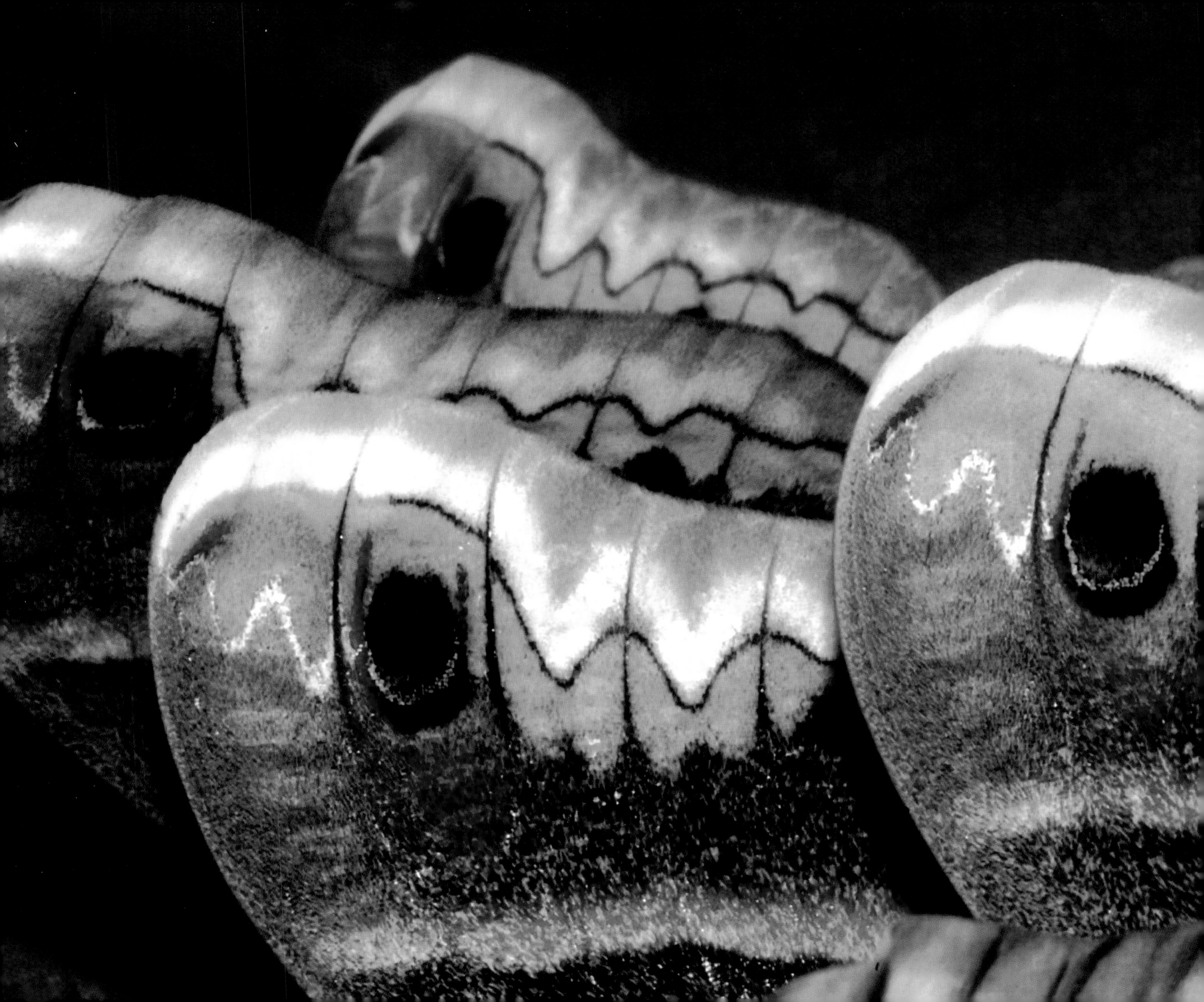

My daughters are grown to women now. But searching back in memory to a distant time, I picture them small as they were then, not yet 10.

The hour was late afternoon or early evening in the impossible sweetness of spring — the last day of May or the start of June. My wife, the two girls and I were sitting on a bench in the back yard, and I was remembering aloud one of the wonders of my own early years.

There was a spell in childhood when my mother was hospitalized for surgery and bedfast for some weeks afterward. During her recovery, I lived with Sue and Guy Middleton, my grandparents, on their little acreage out past the city's edge. That's where I first saw the great moths that inhabit the middle region of our country.

Later, through all the years of my growing up in a bungalow in an ordinary city neighborhood, I occasionally would see them again. In the last hour's dreaming before bed, I would lie on the slatted wooden porch swing and they would appear, immense, heavy-bodied, out of the wrapping dark and fling themselves against the screen of the porch — the eye-winged Polyphemus, the rarer Luna — giant apparitions of the night, as big nearly as birds.

So long ago that's been that I almost can believe they were inventions of the sleepy eye of youth. I checked, though, and the encyclopedia confirmed there really are — or were — such creatures.

"There's no knowing where they've gone," I told my daughters as we sat together in the yard. "Gone to insecticides and lawn sprays, I'd guess. Gone to the exhaust fumes of passing cars.

Progress is inevitable. The past can't be retrieved, and maybe shouldn't be. But I could not help wondering which marvel would be finer to show a child: perfect lawns and passing legions of Lincolns and Lexuses and whatnot — or a thing that comes riding on silent wings, Persian-tapestried wings, out of the cool spring evening to seek the light.

"It's a pity," I said, "but I don't suppose in your lifetime you'll ever see such miracles as those."

The words scarcely had passed my lips when an altogether incredible thing happened. Over our back fence and through the leafy branches of the walnut tree came one of the very creatures I'd just spoken of. A Cecropia, this one was, with a 6-inch wingspread — a member of the largest moth species found on our continent.

Magnificently patterned in rich tones of maroon, scarlet, purple and beige, it sailed directly toward us on the soft southern breeze and passed not 10 feet above our heads. Catching a slight updraft then, it rose through the fading light of evening and continued over the house and out of view.

I didn't speak. There was nothing to say. But who could have blamed my daughters if they'd decided in that moment never to believe another word of mine?

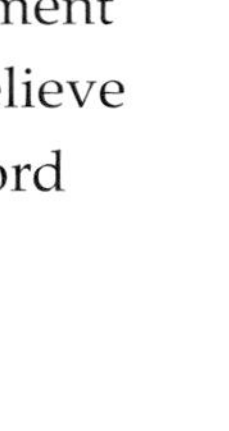

Forward to the present . . .

On a June afternoon — June 12 to be precise — I came home to the city from an overnight at our farm. My wife, Katie, greeted me with some news.

A few days earlier, an upper screen panel from the storm door at the side entrance off the kitchen had been removed for repair. In the night, a large female moth, drawn by the light above the step, had come through the opening where the screen had been and gotten between the storm door and the inner one, then had been unable to find her way out again.

That's where Katie had discovered it. One of our house cats had been drawn to the movement of the moth's wings, which were opening and folding slowly. The cat, Mickey, was touching the wings with a gentle paw, not threateningly but with playful curiosity.

From Katie's description of the creature's size and coloring, it seemed clear it was a Cecropia silkmoth (Hyalophora cecropia). Gathering it up with care, she'd deposited it on foliage outside the door. An hour or two later, when she looked again, it was gone.

On a pane of the inner door were 18 tiny tan eggs, no larger than tomato seeds, strung out in an irregular line across the glass. Lower down, on the wood of the door frame, was a cluster of 35, making 53 eggs in all.

Ordinarily the moth would have deposited her eggs on the leaves of a bush or tree the hatchlings would favor as food. But caught between the doors, driven by the impulse to replicate her kind, she'd done what was possible — affixing her eggs with a natural adhesive to the surfaces of the glass and the wood.

What can we do?" Katie asked.

"I don't know," I said. "I'll make some calls and see what I can learn."

The next three days I tried without luck to locate by phone someone experienced in the matter. Finally, on June 16, through a lead supplied by the Missouri Botanical Garden in St. Louis, I reached a man in Illinois, Ray Kirkman, who with his son had raised hundreds of Cecropias.

"How many eggs do you have?" he inquired.

"Fifty-three," I told him.

"They should hatch in 10 days or so," he said. "But don't look for any more. "The caterpillars get big. By the time mine were in their final stage, I was cutting pick-up truck loads of leaves."

"What kind of leaves?" I asked.

"They like river birch. Mine did well on that."

"What else?" I didn't know where I could cut a quantity of birch.

"Lilac," Kirkman said. "Maple. Wild cherry. Apple and other fruit leaves."

"How do I get the eggs off the glass?" I asked him.

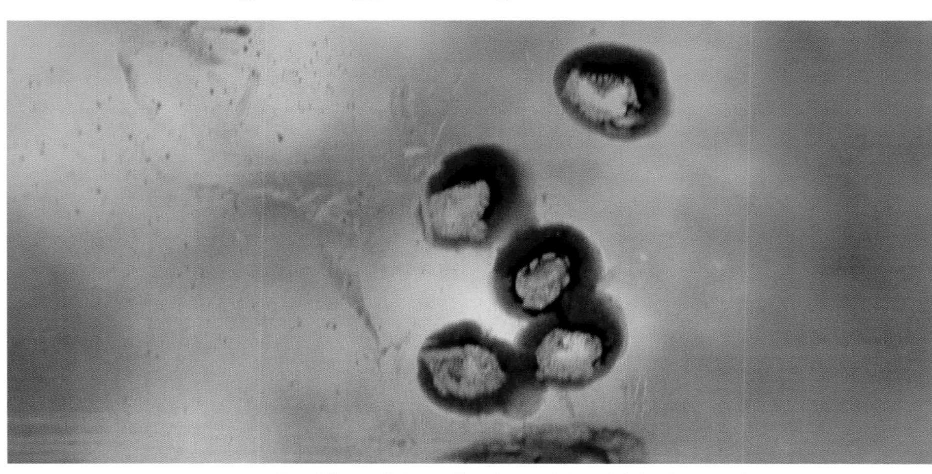

Residue of the adhesive with which the moth attached her eggs to the window glass.

"Scrape them off with a knife or a razor blade."

"Aren't they terribly fragile?"

"No," he said. "They're tough. Just scrape them off."

I did, and put them in an empty frozen yogurt carton with leaves from a lilac bush in our front yard. So this enterprise is begun, though I am uncertain if it will come to anything.

The first nursery.

No larger than a tomato seed, the tiny egg contains a miracle.

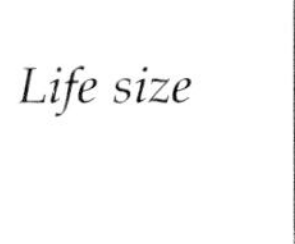

Life size

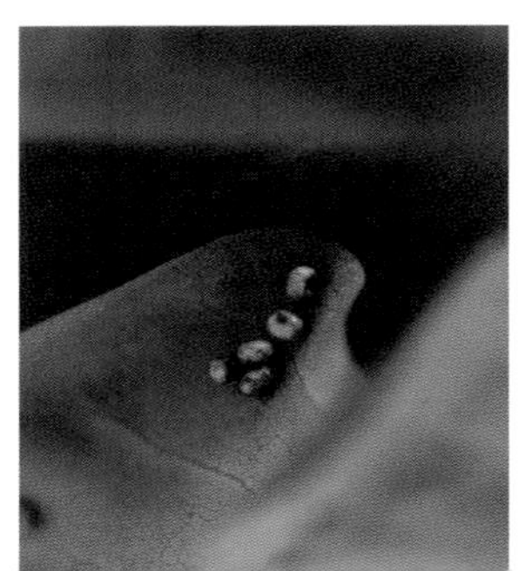

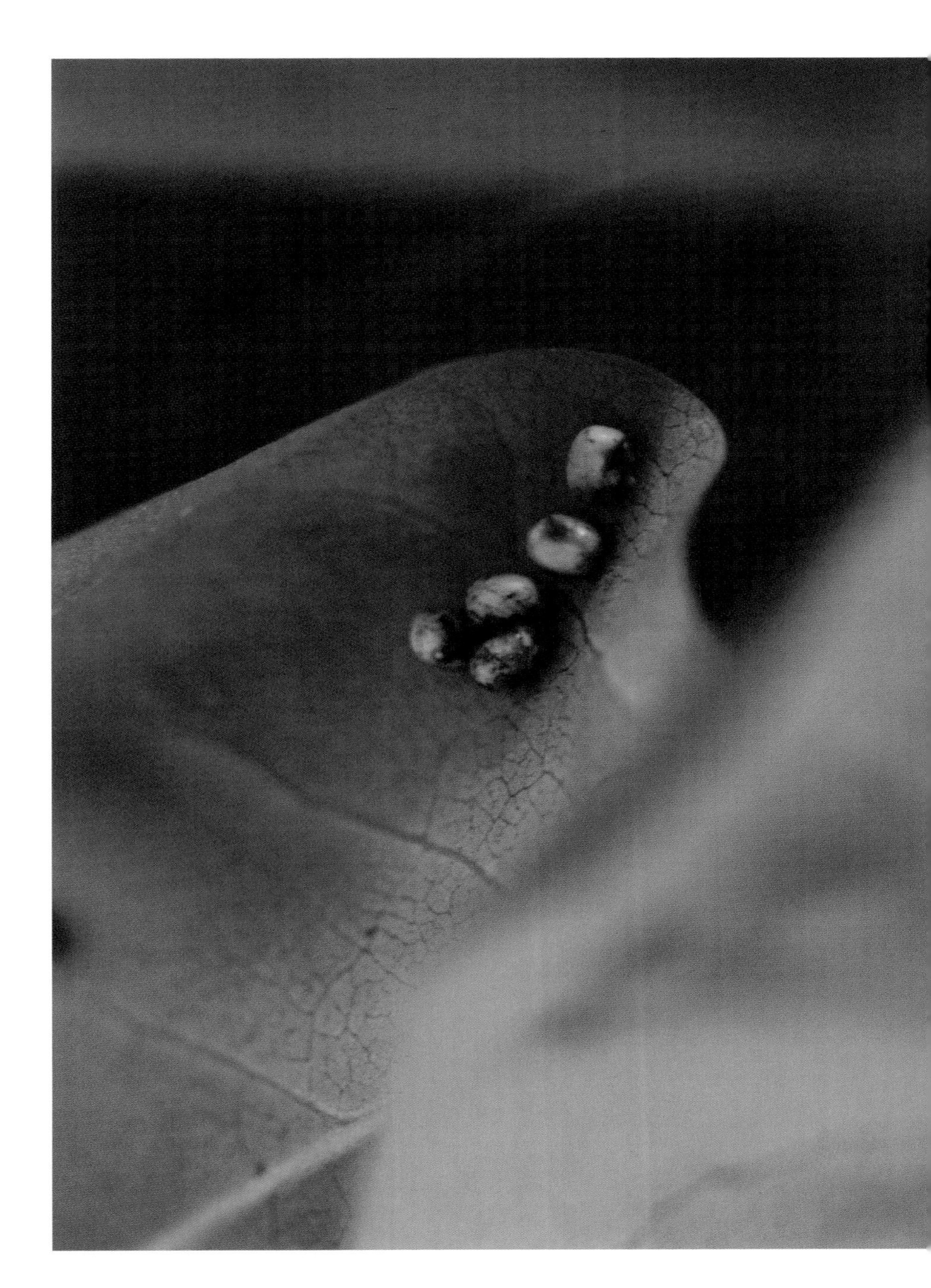

My past experience with projects of this kind has not been good. Years ago, we found what resembled a tiny green envelope attached to a sprig of dill in Katie's herb garden. It was a butterfly chrysalis — the outer covering of a small green creatutre, a pupating larva. We brought it indoors and taped it to the window shade of a room we rarely use.

Inside that inch-long chrysalis a transformation was taking place.

Children know all about the changing of caterpillars into butterflies. Adults have spoken of it as truth, so the young accept it as just another fact in nature — like talking parrots, the distance to the nearest star, the fabulous multiplying power of a single seed. Somewhere at every hour of every day the world over, safe to say, these metamorphoses are occurring in numbers beyond counting.

I meant for us to watch it together. Each day we inspected the chrysalis for some sign of stirring. We had been told that in the last hours before emergence its color would noticeably darken. If it did, we missed that — missed it all. It simply happened as most wonders do. One afternoon when we went to check, the envelope hung empty from its sprig. And there, on the bookshelf below it, was the black swallowtail fully formed.

Someone has said, or I have read it somewhere, that a butterfly does not realize it is capable of flight until it feels the stirring, lifting power of a breeze. In that sudden instant, the thing that used to creep understands that it can ride the air. For many creatures, even sometimes for us, there are moments a bit like that, when in a rush of unexpected recognitions, we feel our possibilities change. But nothing, I suppose, compared to what a new butterfly must experience upon the discovery of its wings.

For the one on our bookshelf, that never happened. In that closed and windless room, it never transcended the memory of its crawling former self. It never flew.

Some days it perched on a round stone picked up years ago in a forest and kept for a paperweight. Other times it crept up to the window and seemed to be looking out, its wings spread so that the light passing through the blue-black background and the smaller markings of yellow and orange was like sun through a medieval colored glass.

At first, whenever we entered, it would give a small show of alarm, standing higher on its legs, drawing its wings together as if preparing for the escape it hadn't mastered. Later, it seemed to become more accustomed to us. One of the girls extended her hand, and the butterfly stepped onto her finger and clung there while she held it higher against the light.

There was a brief discussion of setting it free outdoors. But we were pained to think of it becoming a bite for some passing bird.

"We'll keep it here," I said. "It seems content enough. And they only live a few days anyway."

An error.

Someone raised the question of what it would eat. "They don't take nourishment," I answered with the typical certainty of the uninformed. "They only eat when they're caterpillars."

Wrong again!

Days passed. A week, and more. The swallowtail climbed less often to the pane, spent most of the time on its stone or beside it, moved only slightly when we came near. Then I found it on the window sill – still beautiful and undamaged, but lifeless, having as its final act spread its wings out perfectly flat, as if in a collector's display.

Too late, I troubled myself to do some reading in a book. Not only had there been no breeze in the room. There'd been no nectar, or even any water. Butterflies, I learned, must drink to live. Why else, in the wild, would they travel as they do from flower to flower?

By our concern, it had been kept from being all it might have been. And then, in ignorance, I had starved it. In the face of the truly miraculous, how clumsy we sometimes are.

Each day I have made fresh cuttings from the lilac bush to replace yesterday's leaves in the yogurt carton. More than a week has now passed without any sign of stirring. I have no faith that anything will come of this.

So I telephoned Ray Kirkman in Illinois again.

"It's possible the female wasn't bred," he said. "But don't give up yet."

The female emits a pheromone, a chemical odor that signals her readiness for mating. This emission is termed the "calling." A randomly wandering male, upon encountering that odor plume, follows it upwind to its source. But if the Cecropia had not mated before being trapped between the doors, her eggs — like the eggs of a hen not exposed to a rooster — would be infertile.

"I'd give it a while longer," Kirkman said.

Sure enough, the morning of June 22, ten days after discovery of the eggs, the first caterpillars have begun to emerge. They are tiny creatures, a quarter-inch long and hardly thicker than coarse sewing thread.

The first hatching, June 22

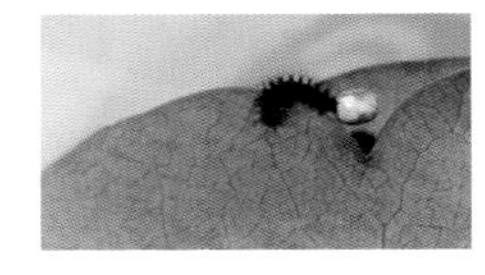

Life size

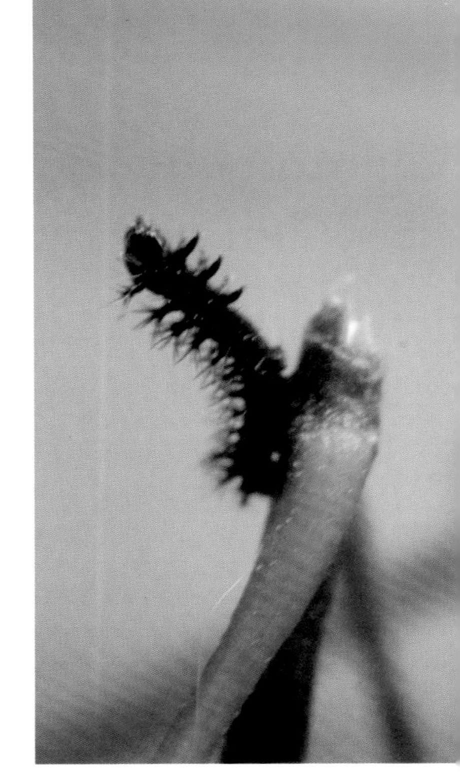

Emerger takes its first look around.

I take out yesterday's wilted leaves and put in fresh ones. More newcomers can be seen crawling over the leaves, but there is no sign of feeding. Afraid of making myself a nuisance, I put in another call to Illinois. My adviser there is patient.

"It's important to get them eating quickly. If they won't take lilac, try maple or wild cherry."

There's a maple tree in our yard. And a large wild cherry tree across a neighbor's fence, its branches overhanging our upstairs deck. I put a supply of both in the carton. And by the next morning there is clear evidence of eating. But only on the wild cherry leaves. The maple leaves are ignored entirely.

Cleaning out their quarters, I find several unhatched eggs and several shriveled little fellows that clearly are dead. The losses total 10, leaving 43 live caterpillars in all. I remove the maple leaves and put in a fresh supply of cherry sprigs from the neighbor's tree. With much coaxing, the hatchlings are persuaded to transfer to the new leaves. And my choring of the herd is finished for the day.

The preference is for wild cherry.

Bold adventurer, with a regular paper clip for scale.

Life size

Browsing the Internet, I'm charmed to discover there are people who actually buy, sell and trade caterpillars and adult moths and butterflies for breeding, and who refer to their merchandise as *the livestock*.

My friend, Charles Porter, is a cardiologist, a leading practitioner of his specialty. But by altogether unrelated passion, he also is a wonderfully gifted photographer, whose work is regularly displayed on office walls and galleries in our city and beyond. And when I mentioned to him this Cecropia project, he decided to enlist.

Charlie made the first pictures of the moth's eggs, before we knew what, if anything, would come of this. Now, at either end of his long days of medical practice — in the early light of morning or soft light of summer evenings — he stops by regularly to chronicle the changes in the nursery.

June 25

The days proceed, sometimes with nice surprises, sometimes with disappointment. For the hold on life of any creatures as small and delicate as these must be tenuous.

Yesterday, when I cleaned the nursery and introduced fresh cherry leaves, only 40 live caterpillars could be found. Evidently three of those I counted yesterday were too late locating their first meal. Those remaining move about actively, however, eating vigorously and producing droppings — called frass — that are smaller than the smallest grain of sand.

And processing them this morning, I found the herd has increased by one, to 41, possibly hatched late from an egg overlooked in a previous cleaning. The individuals have at least doubled in size, to a half-inch, and a faint shade of yellow, evidence of their approaching first molt, has begun to show through their original black coloration.

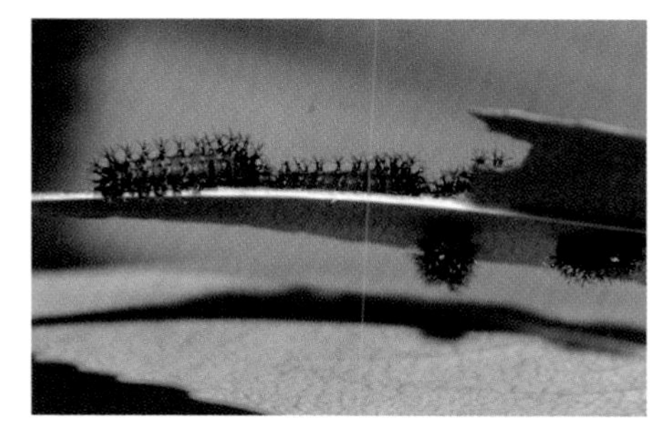

Life size

Preparing for their first molt.

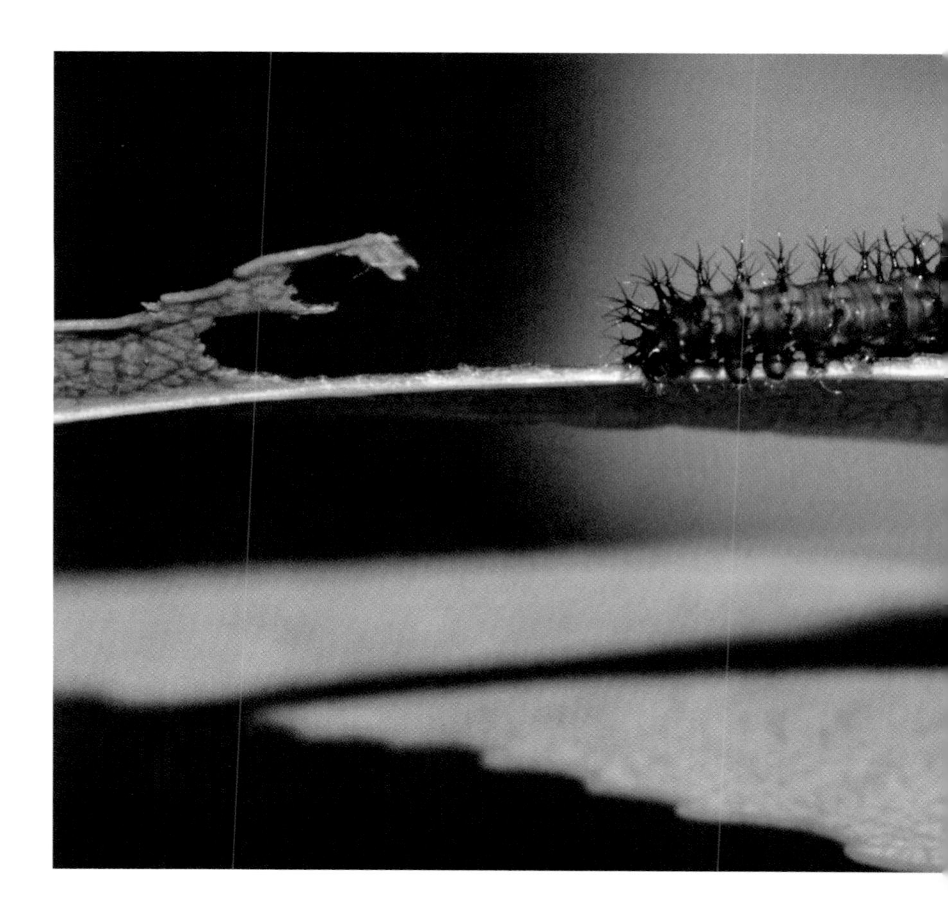

As they increase in size, they will molt four times — that is, shed their outgrown skins — changing their appearance dramatically with each molt.

Today, one bold individual strayed off the sheet of typing paper that serves as a changing station and had to be enticed back onto a leaf and returned to the carton. Now, while still small, they tend for the most part to feed as a group. Although, as they continue to increase in size, I'm told, they will become more solitary.

June 28

One was found dead yesterday on the paper napkin at the bottom of the nursery. Another appeared feeble. And today two more, including the feeble one from yesterday, were discovered to have perished overnight. The mortality seems to average one or two a day now, and is disappointing, but likely less severe than would occur in nature, where young caterpillars are preyed upon by wasps, spiders and opportunistic birds.

Even in the house, fine mosquito netting must be put over the containers to protect the young from their special enemy, the tachinid fly, a parasitic insect about the size of the common housefly. The tachinid pierces the skin of the caterpillar and lays its eggs inside. The caterpillar may live through its stages of development, seemingly unaffected, and spin the cocoon in which it will pass the winter.

The outcome, however, is particularly ghastly. For the tachinid maggots, when they hatch, devour the host from within. And the following spring, as if in a Kafkaesque nightmare, what emerges from the cocoon — instead of a moth of great beauty — is a new brood of parasitic flies.

It is becoming increasingly difficult to find leaves the caterpillars will accept. I've made cuttings from different cherry trees, but those have hardly been touched. Evidently, like the young of our species, the little creatures are very specific in their tastes.

So, leaning precariously over the railing of the upstairs deck, I stretch to clip the last reachable twigs from the original tree. Immediately the herd begins moving from the alien leaves onto the familiar foliage. The count is 38.

July 1

Returning from a brief trip out of the city, I found no change in their numbers. And all appear robust.

They are a good deal larger now. And in my absence the first molt has occurred. In the bottom of the carton, their shed skins are fuzzy black clumps amid the dusting of frass. In their new phase, the caterpillars wear striking new suits of bright yellow.

One still is struggling to molt. It makes its way off the changing paper onto the desk, and then onto the spiral cord of the telephone, from which it can only with difficulty and much patience be coaxed onto a leaf.

Charlie Porter comes early on his way to the hospital to make pictures. I put in the nursery the cherry twigs from the last cutting, stems crushed and saved in a glass of water to keep them from withering.

A neighbor whom Charlie told of our project has volunteered a cherry tree in his back yard as a source of fodder. I'll try those leaves in coming days. I also will need to prepare a second container, as the caterpillars now are of a size to require separating into two groups.

In their new suits of yellow.

July 3

The losses have resumed. At the morning processing, one was dead. Within hours, another had expired, and of the remaining 36 one and possibly two appeared to be in bad shape. Evidently the new leaves are from a slightly different subspecies of cherry and have been rejected.

Using a rake to pull down branches from the tree over the deck, and with my wife holding my belt, I lean far out and am able to clip a small supply of new foliage from the original tree. But still there is very little sign of eating.

I put in yet another call to Illinois. Ray Kirkman says they may be preparing to molt again, and that they slow their consumption during that process.

By noon the molt clearly is occurring, and by evening appears to be complete. They are active again, eating ravenously, and have grown to an inch or more in length. They now show prominent orange protrusions atop their forward parts.

Twelve days after hatching, the costume is more elaborate.

We are traveling by train tomorrow to visit our daughter in St. Louis. The caterpillars will travel with us and will require much fodder for most of four days away.

At a garden supply store I find a rope-and-pulley operated tree pruner that is extendable to 16 feet, and I use that to harvest a great quantity of leaves from the home tree.

By evening, when Charlie comes to record the herd in its present state, I can count only 33 alive in the carton — three fewer than yesterday.

Charles Gusewelle with 16-foot tree pruner

July 7

After the train trip, and installed in our daughter's St. Louis apartment, we found that one had perished in transit, though for no evident reason.

The next morning another was dead, and of those that remained roughly half seemed to be quite robust, the others smaller and perhaps feebler. The night that followed was one of much mortality: five of the smaller ones dead, and one of the larger. One of the survivors had escaped from the carton, but was found motoring across the top of the dresser and was recovered.

In the wild, the casualties from weather and predation must be great. And we console ourselves by thinking that if the eggs had been left affixed to the glass and the door frame, the survival would have been zero.

I'd underestimated the amount of "hay" we would need for our time away, for the last of the leaves from the home tree had been used. So it was essential to devote that afternoon to the search for a fresh supply for the return trip.

We went first to the Missouri Botanical Garden, and we were referred on to the Butterfly House in the St. Louis County suburb of Chesterfield. We'd called ahead, and as we drove in we met a member of the staff walking up from the wooded grounds with a fistful of cherry cuttings.

On the way back to the apartment we stopped at an office supply store to get empty computer-paper boxes for making larger, separate quarters for the two groups of caterpillars. The huskier ones we call the A-Team, the smaller ones the B-Team. A square was cut out of each of the box lids and mosquito netting taped over the openings. The new leaves seemed coarse and dry, and perhaps not very palatable. But they were what we had, and we processed the herd in preparation for the next day's trip.

Life size

Up at 6 a.m. and aboard the westbound Amtrak coach at 8, we were home by midafternoon. Using my extendable pruner from the deck, I cut fresh cherry fodder — moister and much more supple than we'd found in St. Louis.

Working the livestock I see there's been another molt. But the numbers continue to decrease. There are now 16 in the box of the larger ones, seven of the less robust — a decrease of one and two respectively — for a total of 23.

July 8 -12 (Day 17 through day 21)

The caterpillars are feeding more vigorously on the home tree, and producing more and larger frass. Their droppings now are BB-sized, dark brown, dry and perfectly odorless.

Coming to photograph the changes, Charlie is flabbergasted by their increased heft and their evolving coloration. The largest ones now have scarlet tubercles, or "horns," atop their forward parts, and neon blue protuberances along their sides. Their bodies, too, have a suggestion of blue through the dominant green.

A fine display of Nature's extravagance.

Several in the box of smaller ones still are struggling, but it seems likely now that we will save some, perhaps a good many. I've had to extend the pruner almost to its full length, and even so can reach the leaf supply only with great difficulty. It's necessary now to feed twice a day.

One evening, at the day's second processing, I was able to count only 11 in the box of large ones — the A-Team box. And I was gripped by panic that we'd had a multiple escape, a mass breakout. But then I found three high on the inner sides of the box, not on cherry leaves but just on the cardboard, and two others on the underside of the lid's mesh cover.

Another day, on the first count, three were missing. Two recounts produced the same result. So I picked the discarded leaves one by one out of the wastebasket, and attached serenely to those were the missing three. So, for the moment, we're holding our own at 23, though one of the A-Team and two of the B-Team are less active and possibly less hardy.

July 14

A tiny corpse was found yesterday in the B box, and from the A box one simply was missing. The large ones are increasing visibly in size, and now are bright green, the color they will remain as they grow into their next and final skin.

But after those losses, we imagine we might hold steady at 21, for of the ones remaining, nearly all are vigorous, and, if temperament can be attributed to a larva, distinctly strong-willed. When fresh fodder is introduced, they are quite stubborn about moving to the new leaves, displaying a kind of attachment to yesterday's foliage. Maybe it is typical of adolescents of any species — dislike of change, preference for the familiar place, even if it is less desirable than the one offered.

Our optimism was unmerited. We can't know what disappointment tomorrow will contain.

July 15

A CATASTROPHE!

This morning I set the boxes outside on the upstairs deck, thinking the fresh air might be healthful. But then forgot to move them when the afternoon sun beat down.

The heat must have been too great for them, exposed as they were. As nearly as I can tell, seven of the robust ones have perished, leaving only eight. And the smaller group is reduced by one, to five. I'm sick with regret, for the fault clearly is mine.

What's more, those in the larger group have all but stopped eating. I have nearly exhausted the reachable branches of the cherry tree overhanging the drive, and have tried leaves from a source in the city park. But those were rejected. Or it is possible the caterpillars may be preparing for their next and final molt.

A friend of a friend called to say there was a wild cherry in her yard, and I was welcome to harvest there. Her neighborhood is only 15 minutes away. So tomorrow I will drive there to collect samples and see if they might be accepted.

July 16

After two more deaths we have just 11 – six large, five small. The cherry leaves from the new source have been received with enthusiasm by all except one of the smaller ones, which refuses to feed. I suspect there is little hope for it.

When touched with the edge of a leaf there is a slight, feeble reaction. Some sort of black fluid has been exuded from its rear. I isolated that one in a separate container, to prevent others from being infected. Its demise would leave us with 10.

And it is evident that both groups are again molting, for shed skins – wadded little husks – are found almost daily on the bottom of the boxes.

Charlie came on a fine late-July evening, just at sundown — the photographer's favorite light — and spent time on the front lawn with the caterpillars and their containers. He marveled at their size, well over three inches, and declared them the most wonderfully complicated creatures he'd seen in nature.

"If those things were 10 feet long," he declared, "they'd rule the world!"

His enthusiasm is inspiring. Charlie's is a demanding practice, in a high-stress, high-stakes area of medicine. And I am amazed at the energy and the great care he is able to bring to his photography at the end of a long day in the clinic and hospital.

He will be traveling again, but will be back in the first part of August, just in time for the spinning of the cocoons. Meantime, it's essential to begin searching for, or creating, a suitable container to accommodate and protect the cocoons during the long wintering-over.

August 1-10 (Day 49)

Three more computer-paper boxes have been gotten from an office supply store. Following the template we created in St. Louis, I now have five boxes, two occupants in each. All 10 seem to be extremely hardy and active.

The largest have achieved astounding size, 5 inches long and as thick as a man's thumb. Enormous, too, is their frass — almost as large as rabbit droppings. You can hear the pellets striking the bottom of the box as they fall, and the quantity is impressive.

With no mortality in well over a week, surely we've seen the last of our losses.

At this stage, the caterpillars are herbivorous eating machines, and must be getting on toward their time for spinning. The gathering of hay has become a considerable operation. The parents and the daughter from whose cherry tree I'm harvesting have expressed keen interest in the project. Today I took two of the caterpillars with me, and the father made photos of them, and also of their neighbor, who is raising tiger swallowtail larvae on parsley from her garden. The fondness for caterpillars is more general than I'd imagined.

I cut enough fodder today for tomorrow and perhaps the day after.

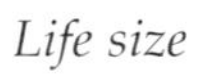

Life size

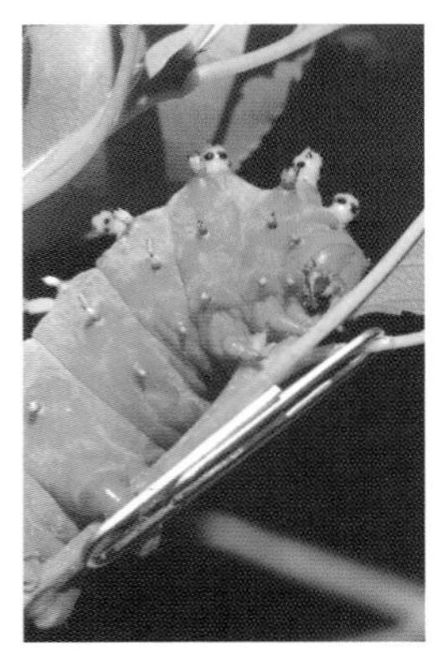

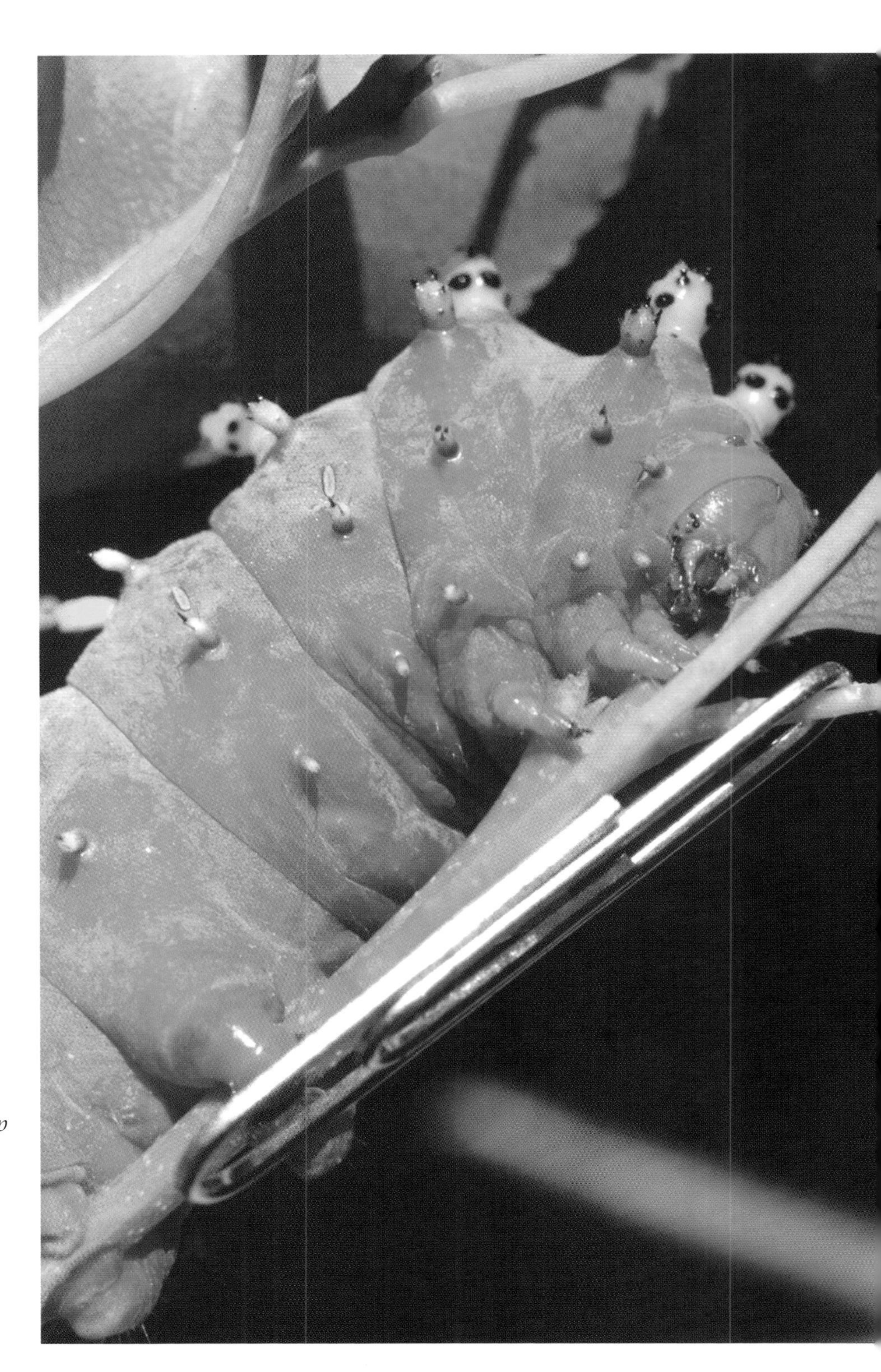

Big Green with paper clip

Little grasping mittens

A face only another caterpillar could love

August 11 (Day 50)

This evening I noticed a large brown splash on the paper at the bottom of a box housing two of the large ones. The stain was large — about the diameter of a coffee cup — and there were five or six pellets of frass in the splash. In any other creature, one might characterize it as an attack of diarrhea.

On a twig directly above, one of the caterpillars had begun spinning its cocoon. I was able to move the twig, clean the box and replace the paper on the bottom. But I was concerned that perhaps I'd spoken too early about the end of the losses.

I consulted by phone with Ray Kirkman, who said he suspected it might be a bacterial infection . If so, in his experience the caterpillar would soon die. He recommended segregating it from its boxmate. So I located an extra cardboard carton and made new quarters for the healthy one.

Whatever it might mean, I could see the creature in the original box moving inside the filigree of silk, working energetically at the structure it had begun. So maybe it will survive after all. We should know by tomorrow.

The rest unfolded in fairly rapid order.

Starting construction of a winter home.

August 12

The one I feared sick has finished its cocoon in fine order. I found it this morning, completed and bound firmly to a twig.

Others look about ready to spin.

August 13

Two more of the large ones have begun coursing around the inner rim of the box at a terrific pace — a great rate, in any case, for a creature that size. Such activity is reported in the literature (what little is available) to be a sign of imminent spinning. Evidently they are looking for a favorable location to anchor the silken envelope in which they will spend the coming months.

August 16

Three more have spun – one in each of the last three days. So a total of four now are in their cocoons, two attached to twigs, two others affixed directly to the inner sides of the cartons.

The remaining two large ones and four smaller ones still are eating, though the smaller seem rather inactive, perhaps preparing for their last molt. More leaves were needed today, and I was able to reach a few twigs from the home tree.

August 17

This afternoon one of the two remaining of the A-Team has begun her work. Fine filaments are around her, and as the day progresses the structure takes shape. I use the feminine pronouns, although in caterpillars the indicators of gender are not readily noticeable. My Illinois authority declares, however, that the larger ones invariably are female.

August 18

Yesterday's spinner's work is complete. It is a fine iridescent white envelope, with some leaves drawn in at the side, possibly for protection. By tomorrow it will have begun to darken to brown. There now are five pupated, and five still active.

Newly spun cocoon

Cocoon darkening as it ages

Next-door neighbors came over today with their young daughter to peer into the boxes and were much excited by the active caterpillars, and also by some of the pictures Charlie had taken of the creatures in their various colorful phases.

I've wondered about the point of such extravagant decoration. It can't serve any purpose of sexual attraction, since the breeding occurs in the moth phase, nearly a year from now. What evolutionary advantage might it confer?

I put that question to Jim Kalisch in the entomology department of the University of Nebraska.

The shades of blue and green, he noted, would blend in with the foliage on which they feed, possibly offering a degree of protection.

But what about the brilliant scarlet of the tubercles, or hornlike protrusions, that are seen on the creature's front end in the intermediate molt?

"In the insect and bird world," Kalisch explained, "red is a warning color."

It would suggest, then, that in the long process of evolving it has been the caterpillars with the most vivid tubercles that survive to become adult moths, breed, and pass on their genes.

August 21

Six now are in their cocoons. And after a pause of several days with no activity in the boxes, the spinning has resumed. It is accompanied by more brown stains on the carton floors. I am newly worried, but another phone conversation with Jim Kalisch at the University of Nebraska is reassuring.

He says the fluid is no cause for concern. It is, as he put it, simply the caterpillar "flushing its system" before starting its cocoon.

Charlie comes in late evening to make some more pictures of the great greens, and within hours another has begun to spin, though just a few of the earliest filaments can be seen. It's common knowledge that the tensile strength of caterpillar silk is very great. Exactly how great? I have spent some time trying to find a way to express that in terms a lay person would find meaningful.

Prowling the Internet, the best I could come up with was a calculation (the source unattributed) that a single silk fiber the thickness of a pencil, if there were such a thing, could lift a Boeing 747 airplane.

In less than a week, the last of the caterpillars will have pupated — that is, they will have encased themselves in their winter lodging and begun their transition from caterpillar to moth. We have enjoyed their "company," so to speak. They have struck us as being somewhat more sentient than we expected, and we've detected what seemed to be certain slight differences in temperament among them — though we have stopped short of naming them. There is a kind of sadness, a sense of loss, to see them close themselves away, not to be seen again until late May or early June, when they emerge as adult moths.

August 27

Today, on the 66th day after the parent laid her eggs, all her offsping are in their cocoons. My home office space seems emptier and markedly less interesting without them.

It is necessary now to begin creating the birthing box in which they will take their final form. They require winter weather to complete their metamorphoses, and thus will pass the winter in our unheated detached garage.

The box must be sturdy enough to defeat any predators that might trespass there.

A secure winter home

So this is what it has come to.

First we took in stray dogs and cats. Then lizards and fish. Then turtles, land crabs and neighborhood children. Now larvae.

And these were not the first.

We collected some once in a tobacco barn. Tobacco worms, the man there called them — although if we'd happened to find similar looking creatures on tomato plants, they'd properly have been called tomato worms.

Like the dung beetle, we are what we eat.

In this first stage of their lives, they gnawed bitter leaves and were loathsome to the touch, their beauty, according to the tobacco farmer, perceived only by channel catfish. *"You just about have to hide behind a tree to bait your hook,"* he said.

But the best was ahead. What such worms eventually would become were moths of the family Sphingidae — hawk moths, or sphinx moths, as they sometimes are called. In that future season they would be nectar drinkers. Ungainliness forgotten, they would come riding on agile wings, swift as birds, silent as shadows. And they would own the dawns and summer dusks of the garden, taking nourishment from the throats of only the sweetest flowers.

We watched, after that, for other larvae. When driving, we found it hard to raise our eyes from the rushing surface of the road.

The nights turned chilly then. Before the freeze, any creeping thing that meant to live to achieve a finer state of being needed to be about survival's business. The last leaves had to be quickly eaten, the twig found, the cocoon spun. At every hand, in the far, clear days and crisp evenings of the coming autumn, one could sense — if one did not actually hear — the cumulative stir of all these hasty becomings.

And being a realist, it was necessary to wonder, *What has any of this to do with humankind?* For we are wholly unlike moths. Search as we might, we can detect in ourselves no amazing possibilities waiting on the other side of winter. To wish for wings, if one hasn't them already, is both pointless and painful. If we creep now, and are what we eat, we will not learn to fly.

That is what the caterpillar must think, too, if it thinks at all. The difference between us is that the caterpillar is wrong.

May 10

Spring arrived unevenly. But as the days dependably warmed, I brought the birthing box in from the garage and placed it on a table in my office, making a point of giving it at least a cursory glance before sitting to the day's work.

This morning, as usual, there was no sign of an awakening.

But at a bit past 7 o'clock this evening, just before closing my office door for the day, I had a last look. And when I opened the hinged front of the box, I was startled to find an emerged Cecropia clinging to the wire, its wings opening and closing gently.

Sometime during the afternoon the event had taken place unwitnessed, 11 months after the eggs were found and almost a fortnight sooner than we'd expected.

I put in a call for Charlie Porter on his cell phone. He was at a benefit for a local theater company, but would come when the event ended. I carried the box outside and hung it on the stump of a branch of the crab apple tree, to let the moth feel the sweet stirring of springtime air.

The first emerger

I must say the excitement is very great — to have helped bring to its successful conclusion a process that can only be described as pure magic. We will keep the magnificent creature no more than a day or two, to observe and photograph, then release it to attend to the business for which it has spent so long preparing.

May 12

The moth has been extensively admired and photographed. Nine other cocoons remain in the box, and we cannot yet know how many of those will yield a successfully developed adult moth. Or if any will.

But the time came today to set this one free. I'll admit to some small regret, but even if this were to be the only one, we would not want it to die a captive. We opened the front of the box as it hung in the apple tree.

The Cecropia remained clinging in its place, wings slowly opening and closing, and seemed not yet to understand the sudden enlargement of its world. After some minutes it fluttered down to the lawn at our feet. Then, in a second attempt at flight, it managed to rise only a few inches above the grass and settled among the stems of a bed of lilies.

Had we kept it too long confined? Was there a window of time shortly after emergence when it was imperative to master the use of wings or lose the chance forever, and had that window closed? I offered the moth a dry stem, to which it was persuaded to cling, and lifted it out of the lilies.

More minutes passed, with very little wing movements at all. Even powerful as instinct is, it must require a considerable leap of imagination — or would for us, though who can say about an insect — to understand that one might own the air. Then there was a change, which we afterward would recognize as the first signal of that understanding.

The slow, small movements of the wings quickened slightly. Then quickened more. Finally, instead of an open-and-close waving motion, it became a vibration, a rapid quivering. *And in a sudden instant, almost faster than the eye could register, the moth was gone from the twig — gone not as a tentative, fluttering thing, but as a powerful, fully accomplished master of the sky.*

Up against the afternoon clouds it rose, 50 feet or more, over the houses and the towering trees on the far side of the street and out of view. What the moth experienced can't be known. For us, it was pure exultation.

By evening, a second Cecropia had come out of its cocoon.

Pre-flight perch

Preparing for launch

The first flawed attempt

May 16

The first moth's emergence was this past Monday. Wednesday was the day of that one's release and the appearance of the second. Others have followed in rapid order: the third and fourth on Thursday, the fifth on Friday and the sixth and seventh on Saturday.

As of today, Sunday, we have released a total of six – three males and three females. In their adult phase, the genders are easily identified. Besides their somewhat greater wing span, the females have markedly distended abdomens, filled with eggs. The fern-like antennae of the males, which enable them to detect at a distance the chemical "calling" of a breeding female, are quite noticeably the larger.

A female that emerged on Saturday will be released tomorrow. Three intact cocoons remain in the box.

Hatchmates together, like planes poised on a carrier's deck.

The female, her abdomen distended with eggs

The male, great antennae alert for the "calling"

May 17

Our intention was to capture the initial moment of flight. But that is harder than might be imagined. The screened front of the box was lowered. After only a few preliminary movements of her wings, the moth began that intense quivering. In an instant, then, she levitated through the leafy branches of the crab apple tree, and the chance was lost.

The female in the lilac bush

She did not bear off toward some far destination, though. After making a high tour over the neighbors' house and yard, she circled back and landed in the foliage of our lilac bush, not 10 steps from where she'd been released. We left her there undisturbed.

May 18

It stormed in the night. I went out in the drizzly morning to see how the moth had survived. She still was where she'd been last evening, under a cluster of leaves in the lilac.

But she was not alone. Sometime while we'd slept, she had put out her scent, and a male had responded to the "calling." There was no knowing if the newcomer was a wild moth, or one that we had raised and earlier released. In any case, the two of them were joined there in the leafy boudoir of the bush.

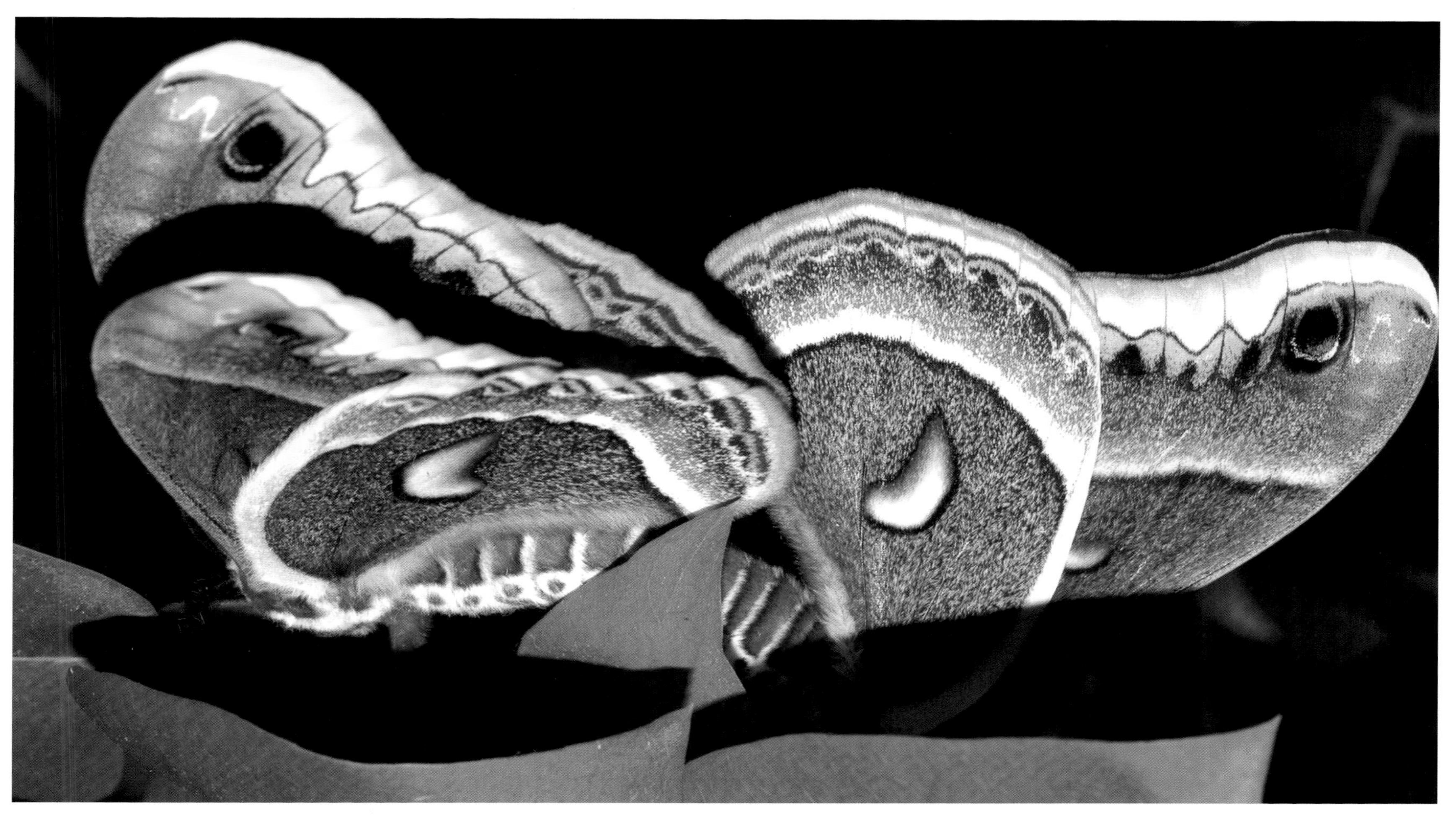

The "calling" answered, two Cecropias are joined in mating.

According to the literature, the mating would last from one night until darkness of the next. Rain continued through much of the day. Between showers, we went out to see if they still were there, and to photograph the pair. Occupied with that, I neglected checking the box until shortly before noon. And found, then, that an eighth moth, another female, had emerged.

By late afternoon the clouds had blown through, the sky had cleared, and we released her. Finally, before bed, I went out a last time, barefoot and with a flashlight, to the lilac bush. The mating pair had disappeared, as the literature said they would – gone to navigate the darkness in whatever might remain of their short lives.

Having no functioning mouth parts, the adult moths cannot eat. They live only about a week — their destiny being simply to fly, to mate and replicate their kind.

Two intact cocoons remain in the box.

May 22

Late afternoon today, the ninth Cecropia was found outside its cocoon and clinging to a twig, drying its patterned wings, the last male. We will release it tomorrow morning.

June 4

As of yesterday, it had been a dozen days since the last emergence. Daily I had checked the box on the table in my office, but there was no activity. All the other cocoons had turned a dusky brown in the days and weeks after spinning. But the one remaining was different — still a pristine, silky white. For whatever reason, it appeared that one was not destined to yield a moth.

It was a bearable disappointment. Of the 10 caterpillars we'd raised successfully, nine had flown and presumably had found a mate. I could not help thinking that in nature the rate of survival might well have been a good deal less. I returned the box to the garage for storage, on the odd chance we might someday repeat this adventure.

But this afternoon, out working in the yard, I was overtaken by a presentiment. It sounds contrived, I know, but it's true. For whatever reason — intuition, or just a sudden unreasonable hope — I was moved to go to the garage for one last look.

And there was the tenth and final Cecropia, a female, legs gripping the wire of the box front, noticeably larger in body and wing than any of the others.

The last and greatest moth

June 5

Today she left us, on an afternoon of sweet sunlight and gentle breeze. She seemed to understand the possibility of flight sooner than the ones before. Just a few easy flexings of her splendid wings, then a moment of that quivering. And almost without any preliminaries she was away, far above the houses, over a towering oak across the street, and gone.

It has been 51 weeks to the day since the parent moth deposited her hope of posterity on the glass of our kitchen door. How many moths will these ten produce? I have no idea. But this much I know: If I were a poet, which I'm not, I could write a whole lifetime without ever releasing that much beauty into the world.

Somewhere, now, the successor generation has replicated that act of faith. Endlessly the miracle repeats. And to have been privileged to witness it is the nearest we'll ever come to having wings.

For the entire series of Cecropia images go to www.CharlesPorterPhotography.com and click MOTHS. See also a more complete folio of photographic art by Charles Porter.

Other books by C. W. Gusewelle

A Paris Notebook
An Africa Notebook
Quick as Shadows Passing
Far From Any Coast
A Great Current Running: The Lena River Expedition
A Buick in the Kitchen
On the Way to Other Country
The Rufus Chronicle
Another Cat at the Door
A Little Christmas Music

A BRIEF MOTH-WATCHER'S GUIDE

Although sometimes seen in early morning or at the twilight hour, nearly all moths are most active during the night. They are attracted to the light, but the likelihood of a random sighting in the glow of a porch bulb is uncertain at best. Better success can be achieved by "baiting."

The largest moths of North America — silk moths of the family *Saturniidae*, to which the Cecropia belongs — emerge in their adult phase with no functioning mouth parts, and thus are less readily baited.

However, many other attractive species are nectar drinkers, drawn to sweet odors. Recipes for the bait are varied; most include brown sugar and maple syrup or molasses, sometimes mixed with overripe crushed fruit. The mixture should be brushed on tree trunks in late afternoon, in areas to be visited later with a flashlight.

Moth-watching can be a rewarding and educational activity, though it may interfere a bit with sleep. Books to aid in identification can be found in most libraries or ordered online. One attractive choice is *Discovering Moths: Nighttime Jewels in Your Own Backyard*, by John Himmelman (Down East Books, 2002).

Use the following pages to record the place, date, hour and circumstances of your own sightings.

Species	Place Seen	Date & Hour	Bait (if used)	Notes

Species	Place Seen	Date & Hour	Bait (if used)	Notes

Species	Place Seen	Date & Hour	Bait (if used)	Notes